Out of Bed
and
Back Again!

A read along sticker book

You'll love to

DRESS AND UNDRESS THE BUNNIES

with 24 big bright vinyl
peel-off stickers!

B
W
J

Amye Rosenberg

Hello! I am Anna and this is Ben.
We are so excited. Grandad is taking us out for the day. Please help us take off our pyjamas. You can leave them on the bed.

Jim-jams on please! Thank you Grandad for a super day out. Good night!

Next we wash. Then we brush our teeth.
Our underwear is on the stool. Please help us put it on.

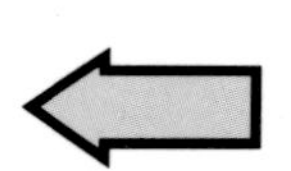

We brush our teeth and take off our underwear.
We put it on the stool.

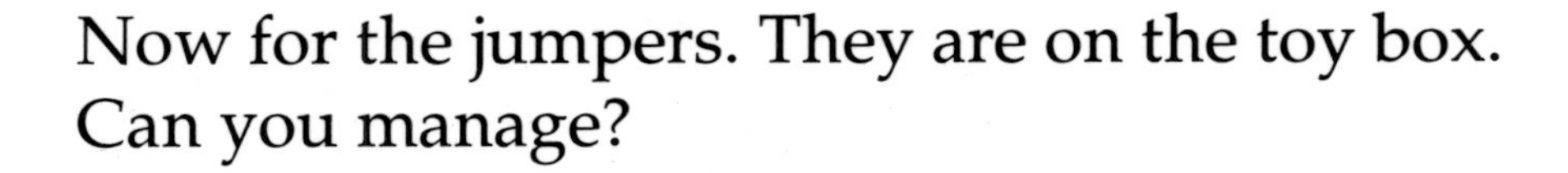

Now for the jumpers. They are on the toy box.
Can you manage?

We pull off our jumpers. We leave them on the toy box.

Our trousers are on the chair.
We put them on and head downstairs.

Will you help us take our trousers off?
You can leave them on the chair.

Where are our shoes? Let's put them on.
Mummy is making breakfast. There's a lovely smell!
Let's see what it is.

We kick off our shoes.
It's bedtime now so up the stairs we go!

"My, my," says Mummy. "You got dressed quickly today."
Mummy gives us cereal and toast. When we finish,
we put our bowls back on the tray.

Mummy has made a delicious supper of soup and bread.
We remember to put our empty bowls on the tray.

Grandad's here! Yippee! We're about to go,
Grandad hasn't told us where we are going yet.
Will you help us put on our coats?

Our coats need hanging up too, please.

And our hats please! We're on our way! "I have a surprise for you today, we are going to the park," says Grandad.

We're home.
Will you put our hats back on the pegs for us?

In the park, Grandad opens his bag.
Surprise! It is full of toys for us to play with.
Even Grandad likes to play with toys.

It's time to go home now. We put our new toys back in the bag. "Thank you, Grandad!" we giggle. "We've had lots of fun." Grandad smiles. "So have I. Let's do this again soon," he says.

B
W
J

This edition published by
Brown Wells & Jacobs Limited
2 Vermont Road London SE19 3SR

Printed in Germany.